THIS ACU TRAINING SESSION ISN'T GOING TOO WELL.
CAN YOU SPOT THE SEVEN DIFFERENCES BETWEEN
THE TWO PICTURES?

JURASSIC WORLD BOSS SIMON MASRANI WANTS YOU TO DESIGN A NEW ATTRACTION FOR HIS PARK. IT COULD BE A NEW RIDE OR A RESTAURANT OR EVEN A NEW DINOSAUR. DRAW IT HERE.

IT MUST BE SOMETHING THAT WILL BRING LOADS OF TOURISTS IN!

HOW ABOUT ... FREE PIZZA?

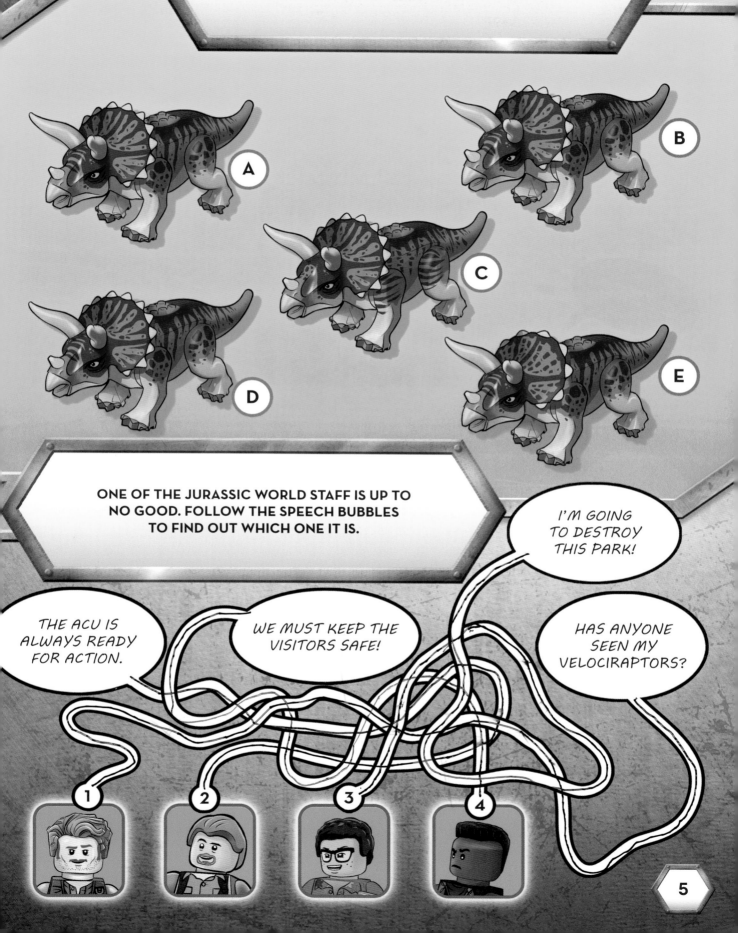

CROSS OUT ALL THE NUMBERS FROM ONE TO
NINE BELOW, THEN WRITE DOWN WHAT'S LEFT
TO FIND OUT WHAT THIS DINOSAUR IS CALLED.

234D6718L9O5P8H9O3S23A18U8R56U46S7

....

LOOK AT THE PICTURE OF LITTLE BLUE ON THE
LEFT-HAND SCREEN AND USE IT TO SPOT A MISTAKE
IN EACH OF THE FIVE PICTURES ON THE RIGHT.

A FIRST DAY TO REMEMBER

SINJIN PRESCOTT HAS FOUND A MAP LEADING TO HIDDEN TREASURE ON ISLA NUBLAR, BUT IS THERE ONLY ONE COPY? SEE IF ANY OF THE OTHER MAPS MATCH HIS.

B

A

C

D

E

CAN YOU FIND THE ODD ONE OUT IN EACH ROW OF ACU GUARDS?

THE BABY *VELOCIRAPTORS* WANT TO PLAY.
CAN YOU DRAW SOME TOYS FOR THEM?

THREE CARNIVORES HAVE ESCAPED! DRAW BARS
OVER THEIR PICTURES TO PROTECT THE HERBIVORES.
(CLUE: THE BOXES AROUND THE CARNIVORES
ARE ALL THE SAME SHAPE.)

13

OWEN AND CLAIRE ARE TRYING TO TRACK DOWN SINJIN PRESCOTT BEFORE HE CAN FIND THE TREASURE. HELP THEM BY FOLLOWING THE PATH MARKED OUT WITH PICTURES OF SINJIN. THE FIRST FEW STEPS HAVE BEEN DONE FOR YOU.

START

14

USE THE KEY TO COLOUR IN THIS PICTURE AND REVEAL THE DINOSAUR THIS ACU GUARD IS LOOKING FOR.

1   3   5

2   4

OFF TARGET

HELP THIS ACU GUARD DODGE THE CARNIVORES.
HE CAN ONLY FOLLOW THE PATTERN SHOWN BELOW.
GOOD LUCK!

START

FINISH

ONLY SIX OF THE ITEMS BELOW ARE USED BY THE
ACU GUARDS AT WORK. CAN YOU CIRCLE THEM?

THIS ACU GUARD IS FISHING, BUT NOT FOR A GIANT *MESOSAURUS*! CAN YOU SPOT THE THREE FISH IN THE WATER?

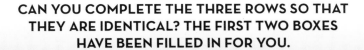

CAN YOU COMPLETE THE THREE ROWS SO THAT THEY ARE IDENTICAL? THE FIRST TWO BOXES HAVE BEEN FILLED IN FOR YOU.

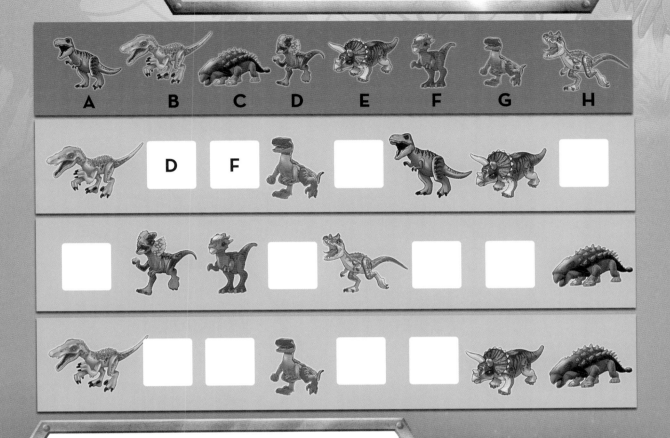

SOMETHING HAS APPEARED IN THE NIGHT SKY. JOIN THE DOTS TO FIND OUT WHAT IT IS.

23

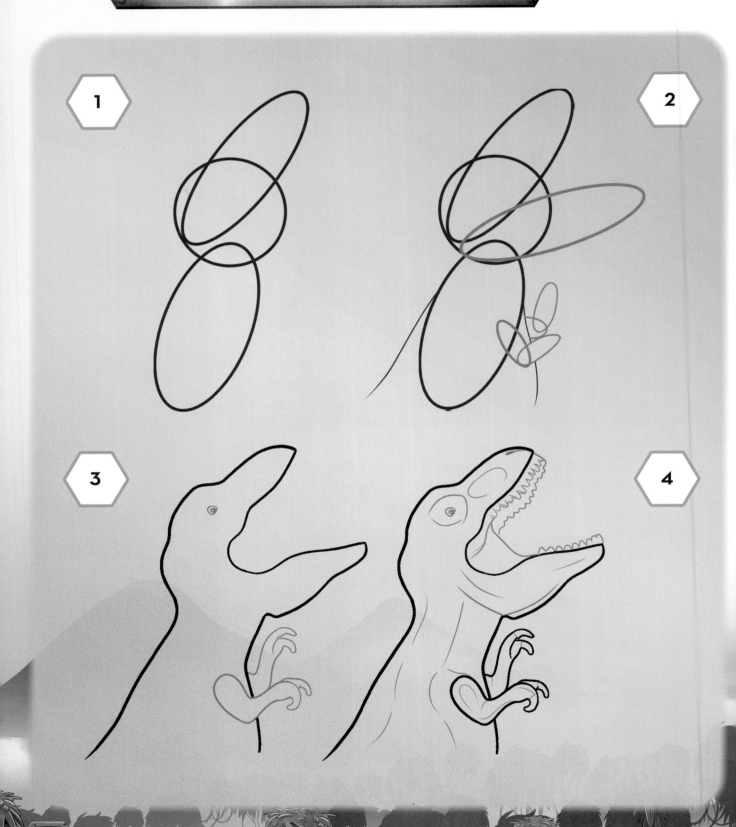

WHEN THERE'S A T.REX AROUND, IT'S USUALLY BEST TO DRAW AS QUICKLY AS POSSIBLE!

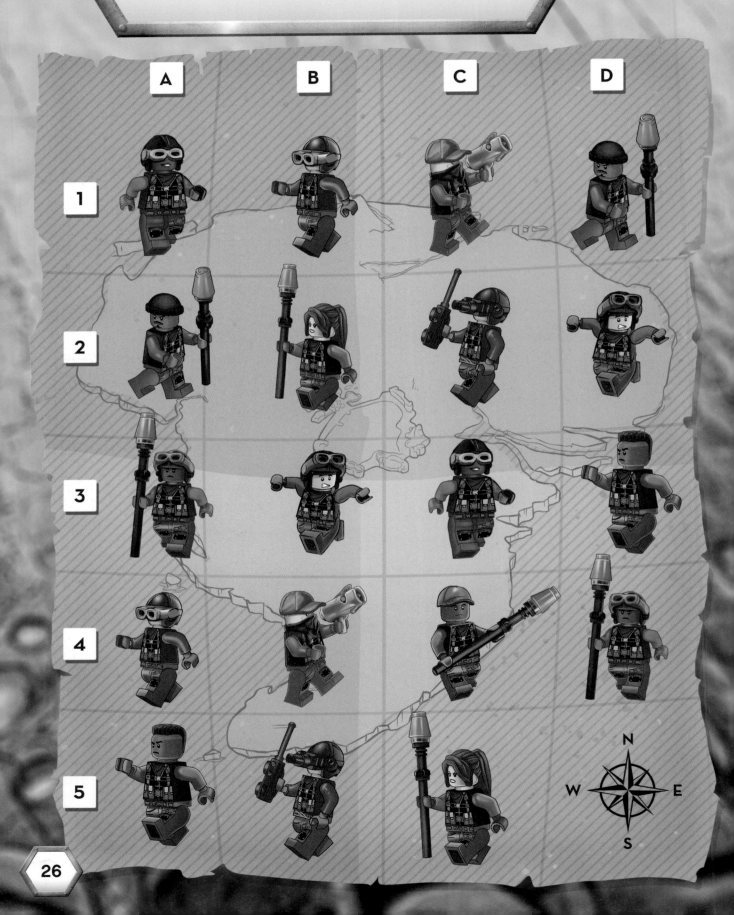

PUT A BLUE TICK NEXT TO THE DINOSAUR AT THE BOTTOM OF THE PAGE THAT APPEARS TWICE IN THE TANGLE. THEN PUT A RED TICK NEXT TO THE DINOSAUR THAT IS NOT IN THE TANGLE AT ALL.

GETTING TO KNOW THE ACU

1. The Asset Containment Unit is a crack security team who keep the Jurassic World staff and tourists safe.

2. The ACU guards are trained to use tranquilizer guns and shock sticks.

3. They are experts at catching escaped dinosaurs.

4. Nothing escapes their sharp senses.

5. They have the very best equipment and know how to use it.

I CAN'T SEE ANYTHING THROUGH THESE NIGHT-VISION GOGGLES.

UM, THAT'S BECAUSE IT'S THE MIDDLE OF THE DAY.

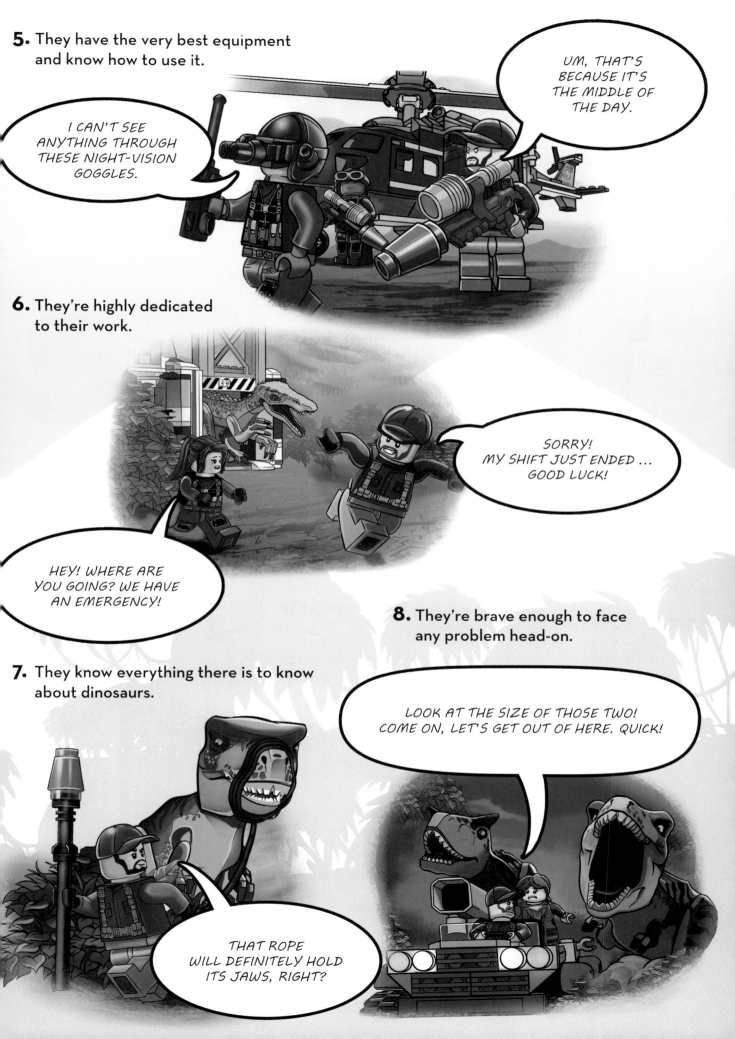

6. They're highly dedicated to their work.

SORRY! MY SHIFT JUST ENDED ... GOOD LUCK!

HEY! WHERE ARE YOU GOING? WE HAVE AN EMERGENCY!

8. They're brave enough to face any problem head-on.

7. They know everything there is to know about dinosaurs.

LOOK AT THE SIZE OF THOSE TWO! COME ON, LET'S GET OUT OF HERE. QUICK!

THAT ROPE WILL DEFINITELY HOLD ITS JAWS, RIGHT?

THIS ACU GUARD HAS DROPPED HIS STUN GUN. FINISH COLOURING IN THE PICTURE TO FIND WHERE IT IS.

SIMON MASRANI IS EXCITED TO ANNOUNCE THE NEW JURASSIC WORLD COOKIES. MATCH THE ONES HE'S TASTED TO THE COMPLETE VERSIONS.

IT'S VERY IMPORTANT THAT I TASTE EVERY SINGLE COOKIE TO CHECK THAT IT'S GOOD ENOUGH FOR MY PARK!

A
B
C
D
E
F

ANSWERS

p. 2

p. 3

p. 5

p. 6

p. 7

DILOPHOSAURUS

p. 11

p. 12

p. 13

pp. 14–15

ANSWERS

p. 16

p. 20

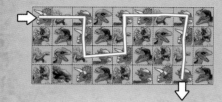

p. 21

p. 22

p. 23

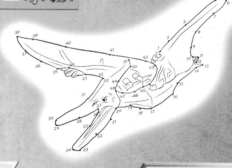

p. 26

4 C

p. 27

 = × 2

 = 0

p. 30

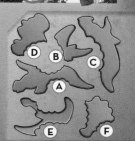